Disney's Year Book

1998

Disney's Year Book 1998

GROLIER ENTERPRISES INC.
Danbury, Connecticut

FERN L. MAMBERG   *Executive Editor*
S. J. VICTORIA VERNER   *U.K. Editor*
ELIZABETH A. DEBELLA   *Designer*
HARRIETT GREYSTONE   *Production Manager*

ISBN: 0-7172-8811-0
ISSN: 0273-1274

Stories on pages 14–25, 36–47, 58–69, 78–89, and all Disney character illustrations copyright © 1998 by Disney Enterprises, Inc.

Pages 14–25 written by Victoria Saxon. Based on the *Pooh* stories by A. A. Milne; Pages 36–47 written by Liane Onish; Pages 58–69 written by Barbara Bazaldua; Pages 78–89 written by Catherine McCafferty.
All stories illustrated by Alvin S. White Studio.

Illustration Credits and Acknowledgments

6–7—© Lee Boltin; 8–9—Erich Lessing/Art Resource; 10—© Lee Boltin; 11—© Lee Boltin; Art Resource; 12—© Doug Perrine/Innerspace Visions; © Fred Bavendam; 13—© F. Stuart Westmorland/Photo Researchers, Inc.; © Fred Bavendam; 26—© Slug Signorino/Slug Signorino Studio; 27—© Slug Signorino/Slug Signorino Studio; 28—Courtesy, The Space Sciences Laboratory Center for Science Education; 29—The Granger Collection; 30–31—© 1991 F&W Publications, Inc. Used by permission of North Light Books, a division of F&W Publications, Inc.; 32—© Johnny Johnson/Animals Animals; 33—© Randall Hyman; 34—© John Gerlach/ Animals Animals; © Kevin Schaefer/Tony Stone Images; 35—© Peter Ralston; 48–51—Artist, Vince Caputo; 52—© Norbert Wu; 53—© Fred Bavendam; © Joe McDonald/Animals Animals; 54—Joy Spurr/Bruce Coleman Inc.; 55—© Zig Leszczynski/Animals Animals; © Bruce Coleman Inc; 56—© Michael Fogden/Animals Animals; 57—© Kim Taylor/Bruce Coleman Inc.; 70—© Tim Graham/Sygma; 71—© Gamma Liaison; Jayne Fincher/Gamma Liaison; 72—© Frans Lanting/Minden Pictures; 73—© Frans Lanting/Minden Pictures; © Jim Brandenburg/Minden Pictures; © Lynn M. Stone/Bruce Coleman Inc.; 74—© Roland Seitre/ Peter Arnold, Inc.; © Frans Lanting/Minden Pictures; 75—© Frans Lanting/Minden Pictures; 76–77—Designed and created by Jenny Tesar; 90—The Granger Collection; 91—© Doug Faulkner/Photo Researchers, Inc.; 92—©Glenn Wolff; 94—IMAX (R) is a registered trademark of IMAX Corporation, Toronto Canada; Sony IMAX Theatres; 95—© Michael Ginsburg/Sony Pictures Classics

Contents

KING TUT:
The Boy King

King Tut ruled ancient Egypt for just nine years. But the treasures found in his tomb provide valuable clues to what life was like in the kingdom more than 3,300 years ago. Among the most magnificent items in Tut's tomb was his jewelled, solid-gold funeral mask.

On November 26, 1922, archaeologists made an astounding discovery beneath the sun-baked rocks of the Egyptian desert. They found the tomb of Tutankhamen, an ancient Egyptian pharaoh (king). The tomb contained four rooms, and each one was piled high with marvellous treasures. Following ancient Egyptian beliefs, Tut had been buried with everything he might need or want in the after-life. There was food, clothing, jewellery, religious objects, musical instruments, and weapons. Also in the tomb was Tut's mummy. The year 1997 marked the 75th anniversary of that amazing find.

Tutankhamen (or Tut, as he is often called) lived more than 3,300 years ago. Known as the boy king, he was only about 10 years old when he became ruler. Because he was so young, advisers ran the kingdom. Tut was married when he was still a boy. Ancient paintings and sculptures show that the young king and queen were a handsome couple. As was the custom, they both wore black wigs. And they dressed in beautiful linen clothing, with belts and neck collars decorated with jewels.

Tut's reign lasted just nine years. He died at the age of 19—but no one knows why or how. When scientists examined his mummy, they found signs of injury. Tut may have been killed in an accident. Or maybe he was murdered. Perhaps one of his advisers wanted to stop him from taking control of the kingdom. We may never know the truth about Tut's

Tut's fancy throne was carved of wood and covered in gold. On it is a sculpture of the young king and his equally young queen.

Tomb paintings tell us a lot about daily life in ancient Egypt. Above: A peasant ploughs while his wife plants seeds. Right: Workers harvest grapes.

death. But we do know a lot about the ancient Egypt in which the boy king lived and ruled.

Ancient Egypt was a powerful kingdom in northeastern Africa. It was one of the world's first major civilizations. At the very heart of this civilization was the Nile River, which carried people and goods throughout the kingdom. Most Egyptians were poor farmers who lived along the Nile. They raised cattle, goats, ducks, and geese. They grew wheat for bread, and grapes and dates for wine.

Merchants, manufacturers, and scribes (people skilled in Egyptian picture writing, or hieroglyphics) lived in towns and cities. So, too, did craftspeople and artists, some of whom painted scenes of everyday life on the walls of the tombs built for the kings.

Egyptian royalty and the upper classes included nobles, government officials, doctors, and high priests. They

Left: An ancient Egyptian artist decorates a vase. Above: A musician plays the harp to entertain royalty.

9

Cosmetic Jar

TUTANKHAMEN'S TREASURES

Tut's tomb was truly a treasure chest. It held more than 5,000 works of art and luxury items. Furniture included thrones and golden couches. A child's chair, perhaps made for Tut, was carved from ebony and inlaid with ivory and gold. There were fine clothes, cosmetic jars filled with precious oils, and games and toys.

For protection, and perhaps for hunting in the afterlife, there were bows and arrows, swords, shields, and daggers— even four chariots. Figures of gods and goddesses were also

controlled huge estates. But the king owned all the land, and he was considered a god. Wealthy Egyptians had homes filled with elegant furniture. At banquets, they dressed in their best clothing. And guests were entertained by musicians who played the harp, flute, lyre, and lute.

Ancient Egyptians believed that when people died, they could take their possessions into the next life. Because of this belief, the royalty built tombs and filled them with everything they might want in the afterlife. They also made sure that their bodies

placed in the tomb to protect the king. One of them was a golden figure of the goddess Selket, with a scorpion on her head. Ancient Egyptians believed she could cure scorpion stings.

Scarab Necklace

The Goddess Selket

There was an incredible amount of jewellery, too. One of the most beautiful pieces was a gold necklace filled with semi-precious stones. Its centrepiece contained a scarab, a beetle that symbolized the rebirth that Egyptians believed would follow the king's death.

would be preserved—or mummified. This was done by drying out the body, embalming it, and wrapping it in linen. Egyptian mummies—such as Tutankhamen's—could survive for centuries.

One archaeologist found something on Tut's mummy that touched him deeply. It was a small wreath of flowers, which may have been placed there 3,300 years ago by Tut's saddened teenage queen. The archaeologist wrote: "Amid all that regal splendour, there was nothing so beautiful as those few withered flowers, still retaining their tinge of colour."

The multi-coloured **mantis shrimp** spends most of its time in a hole it digs on the ocean floor. But it moves like lightning when it spots a tasty-looking fish or mollusc. It captures the prey with its large, strong claws. If danger threatens, the mantis shrimp swims backwards by rapidly flipping its large fanlike tail.

The **candycane shrimp** might look like a tasty dessert to some fish. But it's safe as long as it sits among the poisonous tentacles of a sea anemone. The shrimp's shell protects it from the poison. But the shrimp's enemies have no such protection. So they would rather give up "dessert" than be killed by the sea anemone.

THE SHRIMP SQUAD

Shrimps are small in size, but they are big in beauty and variety. Some are pale pink, light grey, or pure white. Others are red, blue, yellow, or green. Some are covered with spots and stripes. And many are luminescent—that is, they have special organs that produce a pale, glowing light.

The red-blotched **harlequin shrimp** uses its powerful claws to tear apart its favourite food: starfish. The shrimp may eat only one of the starfish's arms before wandering away. (Then the starfish can regrow the arm.) But if the shrimp is really hungry, it will eat the whole creature—even if the starfish is twice its size.

The **humpback shrimp** lives in coral reefs. With its colourful pattern, it blends right into the surroundings. This makes the shrimp nearly invisible to hungry enemies. The many hairs on the shrimp's body are probably used as sensing organs or to attract mates. Female humpback shrimps are hairier than the males.

Shrimps, like crabs and lobsters, are crustaceans. The name "crustacean" comes from *crusta*, the Latin word for "shell." Shrimps have a hard shell that encloses and protects the soft body. Almost all the 2,500 kinds of shrimp live in the ocean.

Most of the shrimps we eat are raised on shrimp farms. They are called "common shrimps." But, as you can see from the pictures shown here, they have lots of very unusual relatives!

The Blue Box Mystery

Winnie the Pooh was ambling through the Hundred-Acre Wood one day when he stumbled upon a strange object.

"Oh my," said Pooh. "It's a box! I wonder if it's someone's birthday—although it doesn't look like a birthday-present type of box. Perhaps Piglet will know whose it is."

By the time Pooh reached Piglet's house, he noticed he had a grumbling, fluttery feeling in his tummy that made him think of honey. So naturally when Piglet invited him in for a bite to eat, Pooh said "yes, please," and sat down for a little honey and some milk. And then a little more honey and a little more milk. Soon he was feeling full and happy.

"Well, it was nice of you to have me in, Piglet," said Pooh. "I suppose I should be going now."

"Don't forget your blue box," said Piglet.

"My what?" said Pooh.

"Your blue box. You brought it with you when you came."

"Isn't it *your* blue box?" asked Pooh.

"No," said Piglet. "I don't think I own any blue boxes."

"Then whose is it?" asked Pooh.

"I thought it was yours because you brought it with you."

"Yes," said Pooh. "But I only brought it with me because I didn't know whose it was. I just knew that it was a box. But now that you mention it, it is blue, too, isn't it?"

"Oh, m-m-my!" cried Piglet suddenly. "You don't suppose it belongs to a h-h-heffalump, do you?"

"I don't think so," said Pooh. "But I don't think not, either."

"Oh, Pooh!" squealed Piglet. "What if he followed you here? M-m-maybe there's a heffalump outside my door right now, waiting to gobble us up! We must hide!"

So Pooh and Piglet hid under Piglet's bed. After a while, there was a loud knocking at the door.

"H-h-he's here!" cried Piglet.

Again there was a loud knocking!

"Piglet?" said Pooh. "I just had a thought. Don't heffalumps and other monsters like to hide under beds?"

"I think so," shivered Piglet.

"So, if this heffalump breaks through your door, do you think the first place he might go is. . ."

"Right where we are!" squealed Piglet as he raced out from under the bed. Piglet headed straight for the closet while Pooh, who had become wedged under the bed, struggled to get free. The knocking on the door became louder than ever.

"Oh, Pooh, hurry!" cried Piglet. Just then the door flew open and in bounced. . .Tigger!

"Hello there, Pooh!" said Tigger. "I knew you were here 'cause I heard ya talkin' through the door."

"Did you see any heffalumps out there?" asked Piglet, who was poking his head around the closet door.

"Who spoke those words?" asked Tigger.

"I d-d-did," said Piglet. "Did you see any heffalumps?"

"Heffalumps!" said Tigger. "Did you check under the bed? That's the first place I always look for heffalumps."

"Yes," sighed Pooh, who had finally pulled himself out from under that very place. "We just had quite a long look under there."

"Then I guess there are no heffalumps around ta be found!" said Tigger. "What made you think there were any?"

"I'm not sure," said Pooh. "Piglet, do you remember why we were hiding from a heffalump?"

"P-p-pooh found a box," stuttered Piglet.

"A box?" asked Tigger. "What's inside this box?"

"I don't know," said Pooh. "I haven't opened it."

"Allow me," said Tigger. "I happen ta be pretty good at openin' boxes."

Pooh and Piglet stood back a bit as Tigger raised the lid. "Aha!" said Tigger. "It's a bouncin'-type thing."

"A bouncing thing?" asked Pooh.

"Look for yourself," said Tigger. Sure enough, in the box was a strange stick bouncing around inside a circle.

"Is it a heffalump's bouncing thing?" asked Piglet.

"Hard ta say," said Tigger.

"Perhaps we should ask someone," said Pooh.

"Good idea!" said Tigger as he bounced right out of Piglet's house. Pooh and Piglet scrambled after him.

Soon the little trio arrived at Rabbit's garden.

"Hello, Rabbit!" cried Tigger. "Look what we found—"

20

"STOP!" cried Rabbit. "You're trampling on my turnips!"

"Don't you wanta see our bouncin' thing?" asked Tigger.

"Oh, all right," said Rabbit as he carefully opened the box. "And it just so happens that I know what this is! It's something to be worn. See? It has straps."

"But what exactly is it, Rabbit?" asked Pooh.

"It's a—a—well, a—"

"It probably doesn't matter, anyway," came a voice from behind them.

"Eeyore!" cried Tigger. "Glad ta see ya, buddy-boy. We're tryin' ta find out what this bouncin' thing is."

"I've already told you—it doesn't matter anyway," sighed Eeyore.

"Why?" asked Pooh.

"Because it's ticking. We're all doomed."

"Oh, m-m-my!" cried Piglet.

"I know exactly what that is," said Owl, who happened to be flying in to see his friend Rabbit. "I've seen it listed in one of my books—it's under X or P, maybe C. . ."

"Hello, everyone!" came a little voice from down the path. It was Roo with Kanga and Christopher Robin.

"Keep the little guy away, Kanga!" cried Tigger. "There's dangerous things over here."

"Oh, my!" said Kanga. "What kind of dangerous things?"

"A bouncy thing with a strap in a blue box," said Pooh.

"You found it!" cried Christopher Robin.

"Found what?" asked Tigger.

"My watch! I've been looking everywhere for it."

"What's a watch?" asked Pooh.

"It tells the time," said Christopher Robin.

"Ah, yes. Just what I thought," said Owl wisely. "Similar to a clock, I've heard."

"Can you hear it ticking?" Christopher Robin continued. "It ticks for every second that goes by."

"I knew it," said Eeyore. "Counts away to the end."

"The end of what?" asked Pooh.

"Don't know," said Eeyore. "Just to the end."

"You strap it around your wrist," Christopher Robin said.

"I knew it!" cried Rabbit. "Something to wear!"

"And see these little hands?" asked Christopher Robin. "They move around in a circle to count the hours and minutes. The fast one counts seconds."

"The bouncin' thing!" cried Tigger. "Hoo hoo!"

"Do heffalumps wear watches?" asked Piglet.

"I suppose they could," said Christopher Robin.

"And what about the box?" asked Pooh at last. "Does that do anything?"

"That's to keep it safe when I'm not wearing it," said Christopher Robin.

"Ah," said Pooh feeling quite satisfied with himself. In fact, everyone was feeling quite satisfied, and Christopher Robin was feeling so grateful that he decided to have a big party. It was a wonderful party, too. The only problem was that Christopher Robin accidentally put his watch on upside down and misread the time, so he was a bit late.

HALE-BOPP
THE "WOW" COMET!

Sky watchers around the world stared excitedly up at the night sky during 1997. They weren't watching fireworks. They were gazing at something far more spectacular—it was Comet Hale-Bopp!

Most comets can be seen only with a telescope. But Hale-Bopp was one of those very rare bright comets that could easily be seen with the unaided eye. It looked like a big blurry star with a hazy, glowing tail.

In its journey past Earth, Hale-Bopp raced towards the sun at 27 miles per second.

Comet Hale-Bopp streaks over the Arizona desert.

Yet the comet seemed to be standing still in the night sky. That's because it was very far away. It never came closer to Earth than 120 million miles. How could something so far away be seen from Earth? Well, Hale-Bopp was huge—about 25 miles across—and it glowed so brightly. "It's a WOW comet," one astronomer said.

Billions of comets orbit the sun, far out on the edge of the solar system. Way out there, they are just large chunks of ice, rocks, and dust. But every so often a comet falls into a new orbit that brings it closer to the sun. As the sun warms the comet, some of the ice evaporates and forms a hazy cloud of gas around the comet's core. Some of the comet's gases and dust spread out into long gleaming tails. The comet now looks like a glowing ball. And

Hunting for Comets

Comet Hale-Bopp was named after Alan Hale of New Mexico and Thomas Bopp of Arizona. Stargazing many miles away from each other, they discovered the comet at just about the same time. Both men were amateur astronomers—not professionals who worked at an observatory. In fact, many of the dozen or so comets that are discovered each year are found by amateurs. Searching the night sky with telescopes is their hobby. If you have a telescope and are lucky enough to spot a new comet, it might be named after you!

the tails look like long hair flowing behind it. That's why the ancient Greeks named these heavenly bodies "comets." In Greek, "comet" means *wearing long hair.*

Because of its brightness, Hale-Bopp was one of the most watched comets ever. Scientists studied it with powerful telescopes and other special instruments. They wanted to learn more about comets. They also hoped to learn more about how the sun and the planets formed billions of years ago. Some of their findings seemed to show that the chemical building blocks of life might have been carried to Earth on comets.

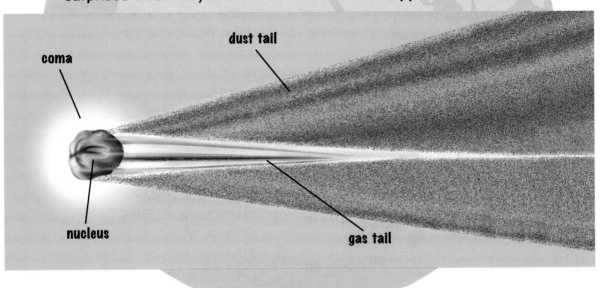

Far out in space, a comet looks like a giant dirty snowball. It has a frozen core, or nucleus, that's made up of ice, rocks, and dust. When a comet gets closer to the sun, the sun's heat turns some of the ice into gas. The gases and dust form a cloud, called a coma, around the nucleus. Some of the comet's gases and dust spread out to form shimmering tails that are millions of miles long. Most comets have two tails, as shown in this diagram. Scientists were quite surprised when they found that Comet Hale-Bopp had three tails!

dust tail

coma

nucleus

gas tail

Tales of Comets

Long ago, before people knew much about astronomy, comets amazed and frightened them. They thought a comet was a new "star" in the sky and was an omen of disaster. The ancient Chinese believed that comets were "broom stars," which were used by the gods to sweep evil from the heavens. The evil then fell to Earth, bringing bad luck. In 1910, when Earth passed through the tail of Halley's Comet, frightened people rushed to buy gas masks and "comet pills" for protection. Even in 1997, there were some wild stories about Comet Hale-Bopp. The next time a comet appears in the night sky, old superstitions will most probably appear too.

The last time Comet Hale-Bopp visited Earth was when the pharaohs ruled ancient Egypt. And it won't be back again for more than 2,000 years. As Hale-Bopp faded from the night sky, stargazers were already gearing up for the next comet, Comet Wild-2. It's expected to pass near Earth in 2004. Only time will tell if it will put on as sensational a show as Hale-Bopp did.

FACE PAINTING

Paint your face and become a black-masked raccoon or a goofy clown! Paint hearts on your face for Valentine's Day. . .balloons for a party. . .and rainbows for Earth Day.

What You Need:

Facepaints or makeup   Tissues
Paintbrushes   Towel
Cold cream   Headband

1. If your "paints" are going to be regular makeup, first rub cold cream on your skin.

2. Use your fingers or a small damp sponge to spread the paint on your skin. Let the paint dry.

3. Use a paintbrush to make fine lines. Apply the light shades first, then add the darker tints.

Just Clowning Around

4. To make a happy clown, first paint your face white. Add a red smile and a red nose.

5. Add freckles, half-moon eyebrows, and sparkle lines near the corners of your eyes.

6. A sad "hobo" clown has a grey patch around the mouth, a red frown— and a teardrop.

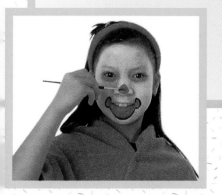

PUFFIN STUFF

You've probably never seen a puffin. These roly-poly birds spend most of their time at sea and nest on remote islands. The horned puffins shown here were named for the fleshy, hornlike growth that extends above each eye.

The puffin might have been dreamed up by a cartoonist. This comical-looking seabird seems like a cross between a penguin and a parrot. On land, the roly-poly bird waddles around on big orange duck feet. And in flight, it has to beat its stubby wings 300 times a minute just to stay in the air. But underwater, the puffin is pure grace and speed. Using its short wings to "fly" through the water and its webbed feet to steer, it can dive 200 feet to catch the fish that it loves to eat.

Puffins are members of the auk family, and they live in cold northern waters around the world. There are four kinds, or species, of puffin.

The **Atlantic puffin** has glossy black and white feathers and a dark, featherless triangle around each eye. It sort of looks like a clown all dressed up in a tuxedo. But the bird's outstanding feature is its huge beak. During the breeding season, the beak glows with vivid hues of red, grey-blue, and yellow.

The **horned puffin** looks like the Atlantic puffin, but its beak isn't as colourful. During the breeding season, a fleshy growth appears above each eye, extending up like a pair of horns.

The **tufted puffin** is mostly black, with white only around the face. During the breeding season, it sprouts tufts of yellowish feathers that sweep back above the eyes.

KIDS TO THE RESCUE

A youngster from the island of Heimaey, off the coast of Iceland, gently holds a young puffin. She rescued it when it left its burrow and leaped onto land instead of jumping into the sea. Each year, the island children save hundreds of stranded puffins by picking them up and taking them to the water.

The **rhinoceros auklet** is mostly grey and black. It's larger than the other puffins and is the only puffin that's active at night. It gets its name from a hornlike growth that appears on its beak during the breeding season.

Right: The Atlantic puffin can hold more than a dozen fish in its huge, colourful beak. Below: The tufted puffin is named for the tufts of yellowish feathers on the sides of its head.

Puffins spend about eight months of the year at sea. They even sleep in the water, bobbing on the waves. In spring, they mate. Then they fly and swim to nearby islands where they lay their eggs and breed.

Most puffins nest on grassy cliff tops along the shores, in burrows that they dig in the soil. They use the same burrows year after year. When the nests are ready, each female lays a single egg. About six weeks later, a fuzzy black chick

BLUFFIN' THE PUFFINS

In the 1970s, scientists took hundreds of puffin chicks from Newfoundland, Canada, and brought them to Eastern Egg Rock, an island in Maine. They hand-fed the chicks and watched as the birds grew up and went off to sea. They hoped that when the puffins were ready to breed, they would return to Maine. In 1981, ten puffins returned. To get more birds to come back, the scientists made Eastern Egg Rock look like a big puffin colony. They set out puffin decoys, and they played tapes of puffin calls. The bluff worked. More puffins arrived, and by the 1990s the colony was thriving.

hatches, and is ready to be fed several meals a day. Luckily for the hungry chick, its parents can hold more than a dozen fish, and sometimes as many as 30, in their huge beaks.

After another six weeks, the chick grows adult feathers and becomes a fledgling. One night, the fledgling leaves the burrow, hops to the edge of the cliff, and leaps into the sea. Without being shown, the puffin knows how to swim and catch fish.

Young puffins spend several years at sea. They don't return until they are adults and ready to mate. Then they go back to the place where they were born, to begin the cycle again.

Beauty-ful Music

Once upon a time, a spoiled young prince had a piano lesson. It was his last. The music teacher suggested that a little practice would improve the prince's skills. "I don't need skills!" cried the hot-tempered prince. "I am a prince! And furthermore, I don't need you!" With that, the music master was sent packing. The prince ordered the piano to be thrown out, too. But Lumiere loved music (second only to a certain downstairs maid), and he moved the piano into a small storeroom under the stairs leading to the West Wing.

The next day, a terrible storm brought an enchantress, disguised as an old woman, to the castle door. Repulsed by her appearance, the prince dismissed her. The enchantress was so angry at the prince's heartless act that she turned him into a beast and his servants into enchanted objects. Only by learning to love and be loved would the spell be broken. The piano hidden in the storeroom was forgotten.

"Bravo!" exclaimed Belle, applauding the most delicious meal she had ever eaten, and the most amazing performance she had ever seen.

"Good show, everyone," said Cogsworth, as if the whole extravaganza had been his idea. "My goodness, just look at the time! Now it's off to bed, Mademoiselle."

"Oh, I couldn't possibly sleep. I've never been in an enchanted castle. And I'm sure you know everything there is to know about the castle. Would you show me around?"

Cogsworth blushed and blustered at Belle's compliment. "Well, yes. I do know every inch of every tapestry and every detail of the castle's minimalist neo-baroque classical architecture. . .if you'll just follow me, Mademoiselle."

Cogsworth and Lumiere led Belle through the morning room, the afternoon room, and the evening room. As they neared the staircase leading to the West Wing, Belle paused in front of a door. "What's in here?" she asked, opening the door. It was the one room in the castle untouched by enchantment—the storeroom where Lumiere had hidden the piano.

"What, indeed?" cried Cogsworth, turning on Lumiere.

"Cogsworth!" exclaimed Lumiere. "I just couldn't bring myself to throw out such a beautiful instrument. And you know what the French say, music hath the power to soothe. . ."

"The Master will have my head, er, works—and your wicks!" fretted Cogsworth. Cogsworth tsk-tsked (sounding like a perfect metronome!) as Belle began to play "Frere Jacques." Soon Mrs. Potts, Chip, Featherduster, and other enchanted objects crowded into the small room to listen.

Mrs. Potts sighed. "Ooh! It's been so long since we've had any music here."

Belle played happy tunes, sad songs, and melodies filled with hope and longing. Lumiere couldn't contain himself. He grabbed Featherduster and began whirling her around the small storeroom.

"*Oo-la-la!*" cried Featherduster, bumping into a cabinet.

"Oops!" exclaimed Lumiere, tripping over a pile of books.

Despite the smallness of the room, Belle's music began to fill the castle. . .even the West Wing.

"What's that?" roared the Beast when the first strains of Belle's playing reached his ears. "Lumiere!" he bellowed.

"Your Highness!" gulped Lumiere. "I can explain."

"You had better," growled the Beast.

"Well, Your Highness, you know that we Frenchmen are lovers of all things beautiful. . .like the lovely Mademoiselle (who is surely the one to break the spell) and, of course, music. And it gives the Mademoiselle such pleasure! We do want Mademoiselle to be happy here, do we not? And if playing the piano gives her pleasure, well then. . ." He shrugged, as only a French candelabra can shrug.

When the Beast got control of his temper, he had to admit that Belle played well. Better than he ever had. Belle was not only beautiful and brave, she was talented and stubborn, too, he thought, smashing an already broken table. She was still refusing to eat with him.

The next morning, Mrs. Potts, along with Cogsworth and Lumiere, approached the Beast with a suggestion. "The young miss might be more inclined to dine with you, Sir," said Mrs. Potts, "if you did something, well, worthy. . ."

"I'm a prince!" the Beast roared in anger. "Who is more worthy?"

"A gesture of kindness," Lumiere suggested.

Mrs. Potts added, "Of course you are worthy, Sir. But all she sees and hears is—"

"Beastly," said the prince, finishing the teapot's sentence as he watched the enchanted rose drop another petal. Staring at the rose, the Beast suddenly had an idea.

That night, while Belle slept, the Beast called Lumiere. "I have made a decision, and this time you will follow my orders to the letter, understand?"

"*Oui, mon capitaine!*" Lumiere saluted.

"Have the piano and all the music books taken out of the storeroom—" began the Beast.

"But, Sir," interrupted Lumiere, "the piano gives the young lady, and all of us, such pleasure! Don't—"

The Beast took a deep breath in an effort to control his temper. "Don't interrupt!" he said in a low growl. "I want you to have the piano, and all the music books. . ." repeated the Beast as he explained his plan to Lumiere.

"Ah!" Lumiere smiled. "An excellent idea, Your Excellency! Consider it done!"

The next morning, Belle hurried to the tiny storeroom. She didn't notice the Beast coming down the stairs. As she opened the door, he spoke. Softly he said, *"Bonjour*, Belle. You will, I mean, will you join me for breakfast?"

Startled by the soft tone of his voice and his polite words, Belle looked into the storeroom before replying. It was empty. No piano, no music books. All gone. Instead of responding to his courteous invitation to breakfast, she turned to him in anger and cried, "Where is it? What have you done with the piano?"

Seeing her pained expression, the Beast hastily said, "I took the liberty of, er, I thought you might enjoy, um, it will sound much better. . ." As he stumbled and stammered for the right words, Lumiere threw open the doors to the grand ballroom. Inside the spacious and beautiful room was the piano, and all the music books were neatly arranged on a shelf.

Lumiere took the liberty of adding, "The very beautiful Mademoiselle's playing will sound ever so much better in this beautiful room, no?"

"Oh! It *is* a beautiful room!" exclaimed Belle, twirling around the room before she sat down at the piano. Belle's playing filled the ballroom and the whole castle. Soon all the enchanted objects were singing and dancing around the huge room.

"Thank you," said Belle. "This was very thoughtful and kind of you. And, yes, I will join you for breakfast."

And from that moment on, in Belle's eyes, the Beast didn't seem quite so, well, beastly. Mrs. Potts smiled to herself and thought, "I do believe there's something there, and it wasn't there before."

A Case of the Giggles

This magician looks surprised because he's pulled a smelly skunk out of his hat instead of a rabbit. But everyone else is laughing—even the rabbit. Of course, this is a cartoon rabbit. Real rabbits don't laugh. Nor do any other animals, except for humans and some apes. Apes, however, laugh just when they're tickled. Only people can laugh at something that strikes them as funny.

Do you remember the first time you laughed? Probably not, because babies start to laugh when they're about ten weeks old. By the time they're four months old, they're laughing about once an hour. Six-year-olds laugh some 300 times a day. Adults are more serious. They only laugh from 15 to 100 times a day.

Everyone's laugh is different. The kind of laugh you laugh depends on the size of your chest and your vocal power. Most people's laughs get deeper as they get older. Eventually, though, vocal cords become less elastic. That's why elderly people often have high-pitched laughs.

You've probably noticed that laughter is "catching." If one person in your classroom starts to laugh, it isn't long before everyone else cracks up. And whether they giggle, cackle, chuckle, titter, snicker, roar, or guffaw, they feel

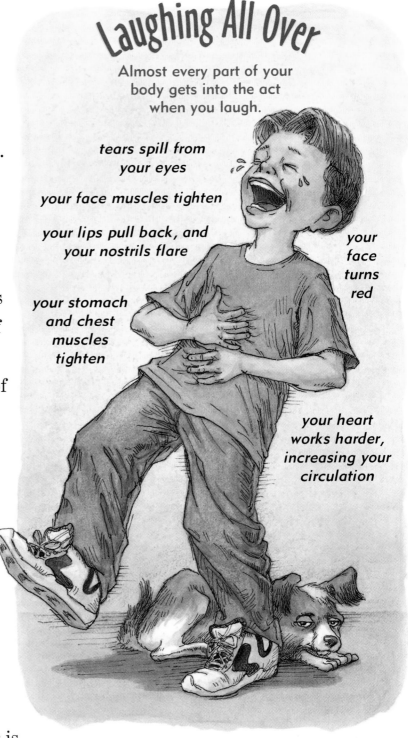

Laughing All Over

Almost every part of your body gets into the act when you laugh.

tears spill from your eyes

your face muscles tighten

your lips pull back, and your nostrils flare

your face turns red

your stomach and chest muscles tighten

your heart works harder, increasing your circulation

In the 1700s, an English teacher advised tickling under the armpits as a way to cure colds.

great. That's because, as the old saying goes, "Laughter is the best medicine."

In fact, it has long been believed that laughter can help make people healthier. Three hundred years ago, one English teacher even advised tickling under the armpits as a way to cure colds! And some American Indian medicine men performed tricks and stunts to help their patients laugh away their illnesses. Today, doctors think that laughter does, indeed, help some kinds of physical problems.

How does laughing help? Like exercise, it reduces stress and gives you a general feeling

Laughing 100 times a day gives your body as much exercise as ten minutes of rowing.

of well-being. It increases your heart rate and thus strengthens your heart. It vibrates through your body, exercising your chest and stomach muscles. Laughing 100 times a day gives your body as much exercise as ten minutes of rowing!

Because laughing makes you feel more relaxed, it helps you in other ways, too. It can, for example, help make you a better student. Studies have shown that students who are relaxed learn better and do better on tests. So before your next test—but after you've finished studying—read a funny book or watch a comedy show. Try doing the same thing when you're in any kind of tense situation. Laughing will help you deal with it. As one doctor said, "We don't laugh because we're happy, we're happy because we laugh!"

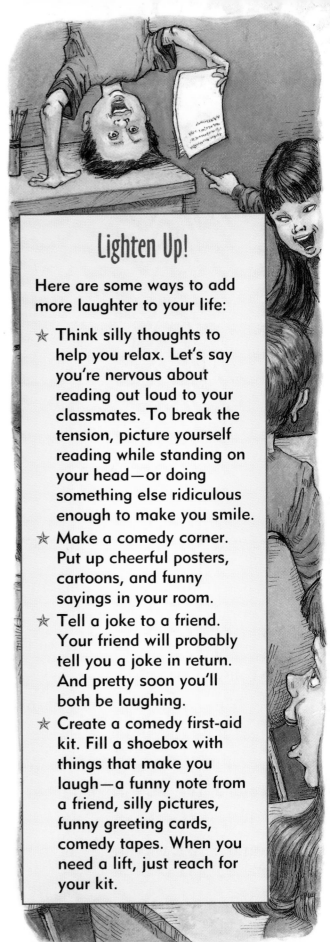

Lighten Up!

Here are some ways to add more laughter to your life:

* ✶ Think silly thoughts to help you relax. Let's say you're nervous about reading out loud to your classmates. To break the tension, picture yourself reading while standing on your head—or doing something else ridiculous enough to make you smile.
* ✶ Make a comedy corner. Put up cheerful posters, cartoons, and funny sayings in your room.
* ✶ Tell a joke to a friend. Your friend will probably tell you a joke in return. And pretty soon you'll both be laughing.
* ✶ Create a comedy first-aid kit. Fill a shoebox with things that make you laugh—a funny note from a friend, silly pictures, funny greeting cards, comedy tapes. When you need a lift, just reach for your kit.

An Atlantic anglerfish uses its built-in rod and bait to hook a meal.

Amazing...But True

Animals do many amazing things to get food, raise their young, and protect themselves. Some of their activities may seem strange and unusual to us. But they're just doing what comes naturally!

● **The Fish That "Goes Fishing."** The Atlantic anglerfish actually fishes for its meals. It hooks its catch with its built-in fishing rod and bait. The "rod" is a long, thin spine that grows out of the anglerfish's head. The "bait" is a glowing lump of skin at the tip of the spine. When a smaller fish comes by, the anglerfish waves its spine back and forth. When the fish tries

The sponge crab disguises itself with a piece of living sponge.

to grab the wormy-looking bait, it ends up in the anglerfish's mouth.

- **Crab Camouflage.** Some crabs are experts at camouflaging, or disguising, themselves. The sponge crab uses its front claws to cut out a piece of living sponge. It holds the sponge on its back with a special pair of hind legs. When a crab-eating octopus approaches, the crab pulls in its head and looks like nothing more than an unappetizing sponge. This fools the octopus just about every time.

- **The Sneaky Snake.** The harmless hognose snake has a bagful of tricks to fool its

The sponge crab disguises itself with a piece of living sponge.

The hognose snake fools its enemies by making believe it's dead.

enemies. When cornered, it swells up, flattens its neck like a cobra, and hisses loudly. But if this bluff doesn't work, the hognose plays dead. It rolls onto its back and goes limp, with its mouth open and its tongue hanging out. When the enemy leaves, the snake slithers away as fast as it can.

How a Starfish Dines on Shellfish. It's hard for people to open a clam or mussel or other shellfish. But a starfish can do it very easily. Under each of its five arms are hundreds of powerful little suction cups. The starfish simply folds its arms over the two halves of the shellfish's shell and starts pulling. When the shell pops open, the starfish has its dinner.

Using the powerful suction cups under its arms, a starfish can easily open a mussel or other shellfish.

The Fastest Fish on Land. The pop-eyed mudskipper is a little fish that lives in mud burrows in shallow coastal waters. When it's hungry, it flip-flops ashore in search of insects. Using its muscular fins, it pulls itself along at the rate of 2 miles an hour. It can also rear up on its tail and, like a frog, leap ahead a yard at a time.

The Fastest Bird on Land. Most birds escape from their enemies by flying away. But an ostrich, which can weigh 345 pounds, has

The ostrich can't fly, but it can run faster than a racehorse.

55

wings that are too small to lift the bird off the ground. Since it can't fly, it has to run away from its enemies. And ostriches are superfast runners! The big birds can skim across the African plains at 35 miles an hour. They can keep up that pace for about 30 minutes. In short bursts of speed, the ostrich has been clocked at 43.5 miles an hour—faster than a racehorse!

- **The Vampire Bat's Unusual Diet.** The vampire bat of Central and South America dines on only one thing—blood. It can lap up twice its own weight in blood every day. It usually

The vampire bat uses its long, sharp teeth to dine on blood.

The female wolf spider carries her eggs in a silken cocoon.

gets its blood by biting horses, cattle, and other animals as they sleep. The bat makes a shallow wound with its sharp teeth, and then laps up the blood with its long, narrow tongue. The wound is neither deep nor painful. Sometimes, a sleeping human provides a meal for a vampire bat without even knowing it.

- **The Motherly Wolf Spider.** The female wolf spider is a very devoted mother. She wraps her eggs in a silken cocoon, attaches the cocoon to her belly, and carries it with her wherever she goes. If the cocoon drops off, she will search for it until she finds it, then attach it to her belly again. When the eggs are ready to hatch, the wolf spider tears open the cocoon with her jaws. The babies scramble out and crawl all over their mother's hairy body. They hang on tightly as she goes about her hunting. The babies stay with their mother for a week or two, and then they scatter to hunt for themselves.

HERCULES AND THE HERO TREE

"Hercules! Hercules! Open your gates!" A soldier pounded on the gates of Hercules's villa late one night.

"Hold your minotaurs," Phil mumbled as he and Hercules stumbled sleepily to the gate and opened it.

"What do you want?" Phil asked the soldier.

"The Prince of Thebes has commanded me to bring Hercules to the palace at once," the soldier announced.

"Come back in the morning," Phil grumbled. "Hercules needs his hero sleep."

"It's okay, Phil," Hercules said with a yawn. "It sounds as if the prince really needs me. Maybe there's a monster in his palace."

"It's probably nothing but a royal nightmare," Phil snorted.
But Hercules was already mounting Pegasus. Quickly, he
pulled Phil up behind him. In a few minutes, they were landing
at the palace.

The prince himself came out to meet them. "Thank Zeus
you've come!" he exclaimed. Then he led them into the palace
and down a long hallway.

"What's the matter, Your Highness?" Hercules asked. "Where
is the monster you wish me to fight?"

"It's not a monster," the prince answered. "It's my little
daughter!"

"Heroes don't fight girls!" Phil snapped.

"No, no," the prince said, opening the door to a large bedroom. "I don't want Hercules to fight my daughter. I want him to help heal her." He pointed to a pale young girl lying listlessly in bed.

"This is my daughter, the Princess Helena," the prince said. "She is very ill, and the royal doctor says that the only thing that will heal her is one of the golden apples from the Orchard of the Sun, high in the Craggy Mountains. But the orchard is guarded by the giant Eagle of the Crags. Her feathers are as hard as bronze. Her sharp talons are three feet long. And her beak is so strong she can use it to snap a tree in half. You will have to conquer the eagle if you are to bring back an apple for my dear little girl."

"Now that sounds like work for Herc!" Phil said.

"Yes," the prince agreed. "None of my soldiers is strong or brave enough to fight the eagle. Hercules, will you attempt this deed for me?"

"Of course," Hercules answered. He bent over the frail girl. "I will do my best for you, Helena," he promised.

Even crotchety old Phil was touched. "Don't you worry, Princess," he assured her. "Why, Hercules will bring you back a whole basket of apples if that's what you need."

Phil and Hercules hastily left the palace. The sun was rising as Pegasus carried them on their journey to the Craggy Mountains. Soon Thebes was lost from sight and the mountains were below them. Their peaks were like daggers. Deep, dark chasms gaped between the peaks far below.

"Do you think we're getting close?" Hercules asked Phil.

As if in answer to the question, a roaring wind suddenly rushed by above them. And just for a moment, a huge shadow blotted out the sun.

Pegasus whinnied nervously.

"That must have been the Eagle of the Crags," Hercules whispered.

"Well, it sure wasn't Chicken Little," said Phil, looking up nervously.

At last they came to the mountain meadow where the Orchard of the Sun grew. Apple trees spread in every direction. In the middle stood the largest and oldest tree, its branches thick and twisted with age. And on every branch, golden apples gleamed in the setting sun.

The orchard was empty. "It doesn't look like old eagle-eye is around to guard her precious apples," Phil said as Pegasus flew in the direction of the tree. "This should be pretty easy."

He reached out and grabbed an apple.

No sooner had he plucked it than a horrible screech split the air. Looking up, they saw the giant Eagle of the Crags hurtling through the sky.

"Fly, Pegasus! Fly!" Hercules shouted as the eagle plunged closer and closer to them. Beating his great white wings, Pegasus flew as fast as the wind. But the eagle was faster.

The great winged horse swerved and ducked, climbed and swooped, but the eagle matched every move.

"AAAAAaaH!" Phil screamed as he clung to Hercules. "Let me down! Let me down! I'm gonna be airsick. I hate flyyyyyying!"

With a furious cry, the eagle lunged at Pegasus. Her claws flashed, and her huge beak snapped.

At that very moment, Hercules leaped onto the eagle's back. Forgetting all about Pegasus and Phil, the eagle screamed with rage. Twisting her head around as she flew, she snapped her fierce beak at Hercules but couldn't reach him. Clinging tightly to the giant bird's feathers, Hercules inched his way to the creature's thick neck.

The eagle raced higher and higher, leaving Pegasus and Phil far below. She plunged and turned. She swooped and twisted, trying in vain to shake Hercules off her back. Finally, Hercules reached the bird's neck. Quickly he unfastened his heavy bronze belt and slung it around the eagle's huge neck. Holding the belt's ends like reins, he dug his heels in and held on. The monstrous bird was furious and tried to shake Hercules off, but Hercules wouldn't let go.

For hours, Hercules held on as the eagle circled and plunged, twisted and climbed, swooped through pine trees and swerved close to cliffs of rock, trying to get Hercules off her back. The sun set and the moon rose, and still they battled. The eagle's angry cries echoed from peak to peak, but still Hercules clung to the reins.

At last, as the sun rose, the eagle's wings beat slower and slower, until finally they stopped. With a final screech, the eagle began to fall, Hercules still on her back. It seemed as if Hercules, too, would fall along with the eagle.

Then Pegasus appeared!

"Jump, Herc! Jump!" Phil shouted.

With his last bit of strength, Hercules leaped onto Pegasus's back just as the eagle disappeared from view.

"You won!" Phil exclaimed.

Hercules shook his head. "We haven't won until we've delivered the apple to the princess," he gasped. "There's no time to lose! Fly, Pegasus! Fly!"

As soon as the threesome landed at the palace, they hurried to Helena's bedroom. The princess lay very still and pale. Her father sat beside her with his head in his hands. But when they saw Hercules holding out the precious apple, the prince's sad face brightened. He immediately sliced a bit of the apple and gave it to Helena.

Helena took a tiny bite of the apple, then another and another, until all that was left was a handful of black, shining seeds. Then, to everyone's amazement, Helena's pale cheeks grew rosy. Her dull eyes began to shine again. And within moments, she was sitting up, laughing merrily as her father embraced her.

The prince turned to Hercules with a joyful smile. "Hercules, you truly are the greatest of all heroes," the prince said. "To show you my gratitude, I will plant these apple seeds in the middle of Thebes so a new tree will grow there. I will name it the Hercules Tree, and everyone who sees it will know what a great hero you are."

DIANA,
PRINCESS OF WALES
1961-1997

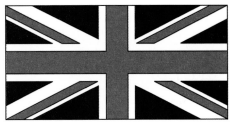

Princess Diana was
devoted to her two sons,
William and Harry.

Lady Diana Spencer, the daughter of an Earl, was born on July 1, 1961. She was brought up in Norfolk with her older sisters, Sarah and Jane, and her younger brother, Charles, on the Queen's Estate at Sandringham.

Diana was only 9 when her parents divorced. She was sent, with her pet guinea pig "Peanuts," to boarding school. There, full of fun and mischief, she enjoyed swimming, music, and especially dancing—she dreamed of becoming a ballerina, but grew too tall!

Diana was 19 and teaching young children when Buckingham Palace announced that she and Prince Charles were going to marry. In a fairy-tale wedding that captured the hearts of the British people, Lady Diana Spencer became the Princess of

Huge crowds enjoy the fairy-tale wedding of Prince Charles and Lady Diana.

Wales—and the first Englishwoman in 300 years to marry the heir to the British throne.

Diana and Charles had two sons—Princes William and Harry. Diana made sure that the boys had the fun and freedom to enjoy their lives, as well as being prepared for their responsibilities as royal princes.

Princess Diana devoted much of her life to people who needed help, especially the sick and the homeless. Above all, she had a great love for children and babies. She often visited children's hospitals—occasionally with the two young princes—and spent hours chatting and making friends with the sick youngsters. She most recently worked to get a worldwide ban on landmines, and comforted many people who had been wounded by them.

All the love and care that Princess Diana gave to others will ensure that not only Britain, but the whole world, will remember her always.

Diana chats to children in hospital.

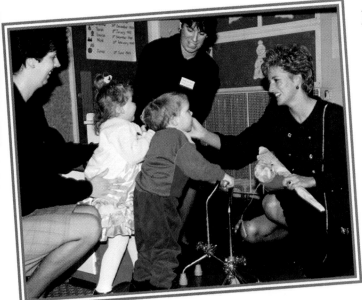

They're Just Eggs-traordinary!

There are more than 9,000 kinds of birds in the world. And every one of them lays a different kind of egg! The eggs come in greens, blues, browns, lavender, cream, and white. Many are plain. Others are streaked or speckled. Birds' eggs are fun to look at. But they aren't made to please the eye. A bird's egg is like a little package for a valuable treasure—a developing baby bird. And as packaging, birds' eggs are close to perfect.

Like the eggs you buy at the store, most eggs are oval and slightly tapered at one end. But "egg shaped" can mean

different things. Some birds, such as owls, lay eggs that are nearly round. Others, such as hummingbirds, lay long, narrow eggs. And many shorebirds lay eggs that come almost to a point at one end.

Despite the variety, all eggs are still basically oval. And this oval shape has two advantages. First, if an egg falls out of the nest, it won't roll away—it will just roll in a little circle. That's important for birds like auks, because they nest on cliffs. Second, because of the shape, the birds can tuck more eggs into their nests. They do this by placing the eggs so that the narrow ends point to the middle, just like slices of pizza.

An egg provides all the nourishment and protection needed by the hidden treasure within—a baby bird. Here, a pelican chick breaks out of its shell.

Once the eggs are laid, the birds need to protect them from hungry animals. Most birds that lay white or pale eggs build their nests in hidden places, such as in hollow trees. Other birds cover their eggs with bits of nesting material. But some birds don't have to hide their eggs at all because the patterns of the shells are a natural camouflage. The eggs blend in with their surroundings. For example, birds that nest on the ground often have eggs that look like pebbles.

Who lays the largest eggs? The African ostrich is the biggest living bird, so it's not surprising that it lays the biggest eggs. Each one is 6 inches long and larger than a grapefruit. One ostrich egg equals about 24

The ostrich, the biggest living bird, lays the biggest eggs. And the shell is so strong you can stand on it without breaking it.

The smallest egg and the largest egg ever: A fingernail-size hummingbird egg sits on top of a football-size fossil egg of the extinct elephant bird.

chicken eggs—it could provide breakfast for a whole football team.

Still, ostrich eggs are small compared to the eggs of the elephant bird. This huge flightless bird is now extinct. But it lived on Madagascar thousands of years ago. Its eggs were 14 inches long and bigger than a football!

At the other end of the ruler are the eggs of humming-birds. Hummingbirds are the smallest birds, and so they lay the smallest eggs. Each egg is about half an inch long, or about the size of a fingernail.

Birds' eggs are so beautiful that collecting them was once a popular hobby. Today we know that taking eggs endangers birds because it prevents them from raising new generations. If you find a bird's nest with eggs inside, don't disturb it. Instead, quietly keep an eye on the nest over the weeks that follow. You'll find that watching new birds hatch and grow is an exciting experience.

A Pencil Garden

Turn ordinary pencils into a fantasy garden that's filled with nifty flowers and butterflies. Your creations can look like real flowers and butterflies. Or they can be unique and come straight from your imagination. To make your pencil garden, you will need pencils with designs on them, lots of

coloured construction paper, fuzzy pipe cleaners in several colours, scissors, and white glue.

Start by drawing the outlines of butterflies and flowers on pieces of construction paper. Cut them out. Next, cut out smaller shapes from the coloured papers. Glue these onto the larger pieces. You can also use paints and glitter.

Glue a pipe cleaner to the back of each flower and butterfly. When the glue has dried, wrap the rest of the pipe cleaner around a pencil.

Now "use" your pencil garden. Watch how the flowers and butterflies wave back and forth while you write—just as they would in the breeze in your garden!

TEMPER, TEMPER, DONALD!

Donald Duck straightened his captain's cap. It was time to sign up for the town boat parade, and he wanted to look his best. "I'll win this year for sure," he said to himself as he walked along. "Why, I've got the best boat on the water!" Opening the door to the parade office, he shouted, "Hiya! I'm here to sign up for the boat parade!"

The parade marshal said, "I'm sorry, Donald, but you can't be in the parade this year."

"Wak! What do you mean?" shouted Donald.

"Last year, Donald," the marshal said, "you ruined the whole parade by chasing Chip and Dale. I'm sorry, but you're barred from this year's parade."

Barred from the parade? He'd always been in the parade. He had to be in the parade! "Aw, come on," Donald said.

The marshal sighed. "All right, Donald. You can be in the parade, but only if someone else sails your boat for you."

Donald slunk out of the office. Who could. . .Daisy! That was it! He would get Daisy to sign up his boat and tell her how to sail it. He could be captain without doing any of the work! Donald paused by the marina fountain and scooped out a few water lilies. Daisy always liked flowers.

"Daisy!" Donald called. "I have a surprise for you!"

"Oh, Donald, how sweet!" Daisy said. "Look, Minnie!"

Minnie Mouse was sitting at Daisy's table. "Oh, how beautiful!" Minnie said. "Pink water lilies! These must be a hybrid."

Donald nodded. "I got them especially for my special Daisy!"

"Well, I have a surprise for you, too, Donald," Daisy said. "Minnie and I are entering the boat parade!"

"WAK!" wakked Donald.

"Yes. We've been taking sailing lessons, and we're all set to rent a boat."

Donald thought fast. "Why don't you sail the *Miss Daisy* in the parade?"

Daisy stared at Donald. "But Donald, what about you?"

"Well," Donald said, "I thought you could be the captain, and I could tell you what to do."

"I know what to do," Daisy said. "I've taken lessons."

Donald could feel his temper slipping. "But my boat would be a lot nicer than some old rental boat."

"Oh, I don't know," said Daisy. "They had some awfully nice boats for rent, didn't they, Minnie?"

Before Minnie could answer, Donald exploded. "Wak! I have the nicest boat in the whole marina! And if you don't sail it, it can't be in the parade!" Donald put his cap over his mouth, but it was too late. He had to explain.

"All right, Donald," Daisy finally said. "We'll sail the *Miss Daisy* under these conditions: I get to be captain." She plucked Donald's cap from his hands. "We get to decorate the boat. You can't tell me how to sail it. And you can't lose your temper before or during the boat parade." Daisy put on Donald's cap and folded her arms. "Yes or no?"

It was a tough choice, but Donald was in a tough spot. "Yes, Captain Daisy," Donald said meekly.

Donald set off to buy decorations for the boat. After all, he had told Daisy and Minnie they could decorate it, but he never said they could pick out the decorations. He bought an armload of royal blue cloth and glistening gold braid. As he walked out

of the shop door with it, Goofy
bumped into him. "Hey!"
Donald started to yell. Then he
remembered Daisy's rules. "Hi,
Goofy," he finished weakly.

"Hiya, Donald!" Goofy said.
"All set for the parade?"

Donald just gritted his teeth
and smiled. Then he ran into
Mickey Mouse. "Say, Donald,"
Mickey said, "you lost your cap."

Donald started to grumble, but he made himself say, "Thanks,
Mickey. I know where it is." Donald decided he had better get
back to the boat before he *really* lost his temper.

But when Donald got to his dock, his boat wasn't there! Some
pink and white boat was docked in its place.

"Yoo-hoo! Donald!" Daisy called from the pink and white
boat. "We repainted your boat."

Minnie leaned over the railing and smiled. "You gave us the
idea with those pink water lilies."

Donald saw, to his horror, that they were even calling his
boat *Water Lily!* He stomped up the gangway and threw down
his decorations. He was all set to shout, "What's the big idea?"
Then he remembered that he couldn't shout.

"You'd better take those things below, Donald," Daisy said.
"And could you take these paint cans, too?"

Donald tried to watch where he was going, but he tumbled down the stairs. As he pulled a paint can off his head, he heard a familiar chattering laughter. Chip and Dale were on his boat! "Why, you—" Donald picked up a mop, then remembered Daisy's words. "Daisy," he called, "why are these two. . . passengers here?"

Daisy peeked down. "They wanted to watch the parade from here. They didn't see much of it last year. Remember?"

Donald remembered. He crept into his bunk. The only way he could get through this safely was to sleep through it.

"Donald! Donald!" Daisy shook him awake and held out a pink jacket. "Hurry! Put this on! The parade's starting!"

"I'm not a water lily and I'm not wearing pink!"

"Now, Donald. . ." Daisy pushed Donald's captain's cap back on her head.

"All right, all right!" he said. He put on the jacket and slouched up onto the deck. But his glistening white deck was covered with greenish-blue carpeting and hundreds of pink paper water lilies! Donald hid in the flowers. If any of his sailing buddies saw him, he'd never hear the end of it. He glared as Chip and Dale made themselves comfortable on deck. Those two! It was their fault he was in this mess!

Then Donald noticed that he was leaning on the deck hose.

He picked up the hose and sprayed a quick jet of water at Chip. Chip went flying and caught hold of one side of the pilot's wheel. Then Donald blasted Dale. Dale grabbed hold of the other side of the wheel. The boat swung in a circle just as it reached the judges' stand. Chip and Dale flew off the wheel and landed in a dizzy heap on the deck. They were such an easy target that Donald couldn't resist. He slid the hose under the carpet until it reached Chip and Dale. Then he turned the water on full blast.

The carpet rose higher and higher until it tore. Water gushed through the tear, and Chip and Dale soared into the air on a huge spout of water! "Ha, ha, ha!" Donald laughed.

Daisy was angry, but she couldn't do anything in front of all the judges. She heard the ooohs and aaahs as water lilies flowed down the spout of water. Then she heard the judges announcing, "We have a winner in a brand-new category. For the most impressive special effects, Captain Daisy wins with the *Water Lily!*"

"Oh, my!" Daisy forgot to be angry as she and Minnie hurried over to the judges' stand.

"All right!" Donald's boat had won. He hurried over to get his trophy, but one of the judges' assistants stopped him.

"Hey!" Donald shouted. "That special effect was my idea! I put the water on the boat! I—"

"Now, Donald," said the assistant, "don't try to take all the credit. I'm sure you'll come up with something just as nice when you enter your boat next year."

Daisy got the trophy Donald had been hoping for all year. Donald had the tantrum he'd been saving up all day.

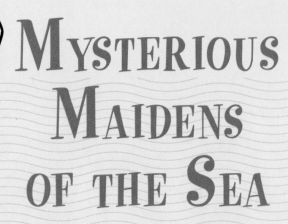

MYSTERIOUS MAIDENS OF THE SEA

Long ago, in days when people knew little of faraway lands, they believed that all kinds of strange creatures lived in the ocean. These creatures included terrible serpents and monsters—as well as mysterious and beautiful beings called mermaids. Mermaids were said to be half woman and half fish, with long flowing hair and a fish's tail. And their magical powers could help humans or harm them.

Sailors often believed that mermaids caused shipwrecks and other disasters. Two thousand years ago, the ancient Greeks told tales of mermaids who would sit on ocean rocks and sing to passing ships. The sailors would become so enchanted—and so distracted—that they would run their ships onto the rocks.

Even some famous explorers returned home with reports of these strange creatures. When Christopher Columbus explored the waters off America more than 500 years ago, he said that three mermaids rose "high out of the sea" near his ship. Columbus was amazed but disappointed. The mermaids, he wrote, "were not as beautiful" as pictures had led him to believe. About a hundred years later, the English explorer Henry Hudson reported that two of his sailors had spotted a mermaid in what is now the Hudson River.

Many sailors really did see something in the water. But *what* did they see? Most probably, they saw ocean animals such as seals, dugongs, and manatees. These animals come to the

Manatees–The Real Mermaids?

The manatee could be described as having a face of sorts. It also has front flippers that resemble arms. And its body tapers back to a tail. It's easy to see how, from a distance, sailors might have mistaken a manatee for a mermaid. But up close, this gentle ocean creature looks quite different. Its body is shaped like a huge loaf of bread. Its skin is wrinkled. And its face is covered with bristles. That sight would be quite a shock for any sailor who expected a beautiful mermaid!

surface to breathe. And they are often bold and curious enough to swim near a ship. Were the mermaids that Columbus saw any of these animals? If so, it's no wonder he was disappointed!

Today, of course, we know that there are no mermaids. But we still enjoy reading stories about them. One of the best-loved tales is Hans Christian Andersen's *The Little Mermaid*. In this story, a beautiful mermaid falls in love with a prince. She loves him so much that she gives up the gift of speech to join him on land.

Andersen's fantasy was also the basis for one of the most popular animated films of recent years—Disney's *The Little Mermaid*. This playful and enchanting movie is about a lovely young mermaid named Ariel who falls in love with Prince Eric, a handsome human. *The Little Mermaid* may just be a story, but it's

Long ago, sailors may have mistaken a sea mammal for a woman with the tail of a fish.

Ariel's Tale

One day Ariel and her friend Anemone found a jar tangled in kelp.

"What is it?" Anemone asked excitedly.

"A coozit," Ariel answered, slipping the jar onto her right hand. "Humans wear it to keep their hands dry."

"Humans are make-believe. . . like land horses," Anemone asserted.

Ariel disagreed, and she led her friend to the surface of the water. "I saw humans here yesterday!" she said.

Anemone wasn't convinced. "They were probably seals. I've read that from far away they're often mistaken for swimming humans." Sure enough, a family of seals were sunning themselves on some rocks.

Ariel lifted the jar. "Then how do you explain this?" she asked.

All of a sudden a ship appeared in the distance.

"Humans!" Ariel yelled. She tugged her friend's arm and dropped the jar into the water.

"The coozit!" Anemone cried, and she swiftly swam underwater to retrieve it. When she returned to the surface, the ship was gone.

"You missed it," Ariel sighed, pointing to the horizon.

All Anemone could see were the playful seals. "Missed what? Seals?" she asked.

Ariel shook her head. All the way back to the palace, she tried to convince Anemone that she had seen a ship. Ariel knew humans existed, and she was sure that one day she would meet one.

a wonderful story all the same. It's still fun to think that there may be mermaids dwelling in the ocean—even if they exist only in our imagination.

This movie audience can't really touch the IMAX-3D images. But the images look so real, they seem to leap right off the screen.

In the Middle of the Action!

Picture yourself in the ocean, swimming under water. Strands of seaweed wave in the water. You reach out to push them aside, and beautiful tropical fish scatter before you. Oh, look out! There's a shark! And it's headed right for you. . . .

Don't worry. The shark can't hurt you. You can have this underwater adventure without danger—because you're watching a movie! And instead of scuba gear, you're wearing electronic goggles that give you a three-dimensional (3D) view. They make the images seem so real that you'll reach out to touch them, even though you know there's nothing there.

You won't find films like this at your local cinema. You'll need to visit one of the IMAX cinemas that show 3D films. The screens are gigantic, ten times larger than usual cinema screens. And the images are sharp and clear because they're created with special cameras, film, and projectors.

Across the Sea of Time, the tale of a Russian boy's adventures in New York City, is one of many exciting IMAX-3D movies.

There are about 135 IMAX theatres around the world. But only about 25 of them are set up to show the 3D movies. Soon, though, these awesome movies may be coming to an IMAX theatre near you!

THE JOKE'S ON YOU!

How do porcupines hug and kiss?
Veeery carefully!

What did the octopus say to his girlfriend?
I want to hold your hand, hand, hand, hand, hand, hand, hand, hand, hand!

What did Snow White say while she was waiting for her photos?
"Someday my prints will come!"

Why do witches fly on brooms?
Because vacuum cleaners are too heavy!

What word do you always pronounce wrong?
Wrong.

Why can't leopards play hide-and-seek?
Because they are always spotted!

What gets more wet the more it dries?
A towel!